The Best Gifts Are from the Universe

A Children's Story about Manifesting

Written by: Kristina Monsanto
Illustrated by: Maria Burobkina

I dedicate this book to the 8 and the 80-year-old versions of myself. We did it! We wrote a book!

"It's a new day and a great time to make friends!" my parents say excitedly.

But when recess comes around, it's hard to find someone who wants to play.

I spend a lot of time with my teacher because she's my only friend.

We collect flowers to build homes for fairies, just for pretend!

"You know, you're the best teacher ever, but I'd like to make friends of my own and we can build fairy homes all together!" I exclaim, looking up at my teacher.

With a warm smile, my teacher replies, "How about we grab a journal and ask *The Universe?*"

"*The Universe?*"

"Yes. *The Universe* is the greatest gift giver."

"With a pen and paper, write what you want and we'll see if *The Universe* believes it's yours or not. Don't forget to close your eyes and believe that your wish will come to you in no time."

Folding up my paper, signed by me, I hope the best friend I wished for is also wishing for me.

To make my wish come to me faster, I say "hi" to everyone who walks past me.

And during lunch, instead of sharing one blueberry, I share three!

On the car ride home, my dad asks me how my day was so I reply, "It was great! I said 'hi!' to everyone just because!"

With my wish in mind, I can't wait for school tomorrow because my chances of playing alone during recess are feeling pretty low.

After school, I like to enjoy a snack, but my trip to the kitchen is interrupted by a small...furry...cat?

"This is our new friend. The shelter said she was in need of a nice family and home."

Wow! My very first pet! This day is too good to be true. Then suddenly...a second furry face appears...

TWO?!

"They said they were best friends and never left each other alone, so we welcomed both of them into our new home."

together.

I'm so happy to have my two new friends; I hope my gifts from *The Universe* never end.

To show how thankful I am, we go to the park to gift *The Universe* flowers.

There, we see many gifted friendships

just like ours.

Always remember, when you ask *The Universe* something...

The Universe replies with...

Yes!

Not right now...

I have something better.